WHAT ON EARTH?

Glass

BART AND LYNN KING

High Noon Books
Novato, California

Editor: Deb Akers
Interior Illustrations: Cynthia Coverston
Cover Design: Bonni Gatter

International Standard Book Number: 978-1-57128-436-5

16 15 14 13 12 11 10 09 08 07
10 09 08 07 06 05 04 03 02 01

You will enjoy all the High Noon Books.
Write for a free full list of titles or visit us at
www.HighNoonBooks.com.

Contents

CHAPTER 1

Living in a Glass House

Sam looked outside. It was a warm spring day. He picked up the phone. Sam wanted to talk to his friends from film class. He wanted them to come to his house. First he called Val.

"Come to my house," he said. "I will cook something on the grill."

Val was shocked. "You can cook?" she asked.

"Very funny," said Sam. "I make great food."

Val said she would be there. Then he asked his other friends. Tess said yes, too. But Nate was not sure.

"I don't eat meat," said Nate.

"OK," said Sam. "I will cook you something else."

Soon Nate, Tess, and Val got to Sam's house. They sat and talked. Sam was cooking on a grill in the yard. Now and then, he went outside and checked on the food.

While Sam cooked, the group talked. At school, they were a team. Their team worked together making films. But they needed a new plan for their next film.

"What should the next one be about?"

asked Tess.

The group was stumped. "I need food to think right," said Nate.

"I will get it," said Sam. He went out the sliding glass door again to check the grill. He left the door open. The smell of the food cooking on the grill came in the house.

"That smells good," said Tess. "Hey, is there some pop to drink?"

Nate pointed outside to the deck. That was where the drinks were. They were in a chest full of ice.

Val watched Tess go out and get a drink. When Tess came back in, she closed the glass door. Val watched as Sam turned from the grill.

He started walking to the door. Sam walked right into the sliding glass door.

BONK! Sam's face hit the glass hard. The glass door shook. Sam fell back a little. He put his hands to his face.

"Ow!" moaned Sam.

"Oh, no!" said Tess. "That was my fault!"

Nate opened the door. "Sam, are you OK?" he asked.

Sam pulled his hands away. He had a smile. "Wow," he said. "I did not see the glass at all. I'm OK. The only thing that hurts is my pride," he said. Then he rubbed his face. "And my nose," he added.

"You're lucky," said Val. "You didn't break

Sam walked right into the sliding glass door.

the door or your nose."

"Glass is odd," said Nate. "It is very hard, but it can break, too."

The group talked about glass. They knew that glass kept out wind and the cold. But it let in light, too. A sliding glass door kept the rain out. Glass walls in a home fish tank could keep the wet stuff in.

"You can drink out of glasses," said Tess.

"And you can see with eye glasses," added Nate.

Val nodded. "Where does glass come from?" she asked. "What is it made of? How is it made?" No one in the group knew. It was clear what their next film would be about.

Glass!

Sam was done cooking. He brought in the food from the grill. There were hot dogs for Sam and the girls. There were corncobs for Nate. "I cooked the corn on the grill," said Sam with pride.

Nate picked up a corncob. He bit into it. Then he made a face. "Oh, my teeth," he said with a smile.

"Oops," said Sam. "I may have left them on too long."

After eating, the group made plans. They would start work on their film the next day. Sam walked them to the door.

"See you all in class," said Sam. "And

Tess?"

Tess turned. "Yes?" she asked.

"Leave the door open on your way out,"
said Sam.

CHAPTER 2

D.I.Y. Glass

Nate rode his bike home. Tess and Val walked home together.

"Hey," Val said. "Do you have a little time right now?"

Tess shrugged. "Maybe," she said. "Why?"

Val told her that there was a bead shop near there. "Let's go see if they have any glass beads," Val said. Soon, they were at the shop. It was called Beads and Stuff.

Tess looked around inside. There were

many beads in all sizes. It looked like a fun shop. "How did you know about this place?" asked Tess. "I have not seen you wear beads."

It turned out that Val liked beads. She liked them a lot. Val got hooked on beads because of something called D.I.Y. Val said this stood for Do It Yourself. If Val wanted to give someone a birthday gift, she could make the gift herself.

"A bead shop is a great place to make gifts," Val said. "I can choose the beads myself. I can make a D.I.Y. gift. These gifts are things you can wear. You can put them on your neck or wrist."

Tess picked up some red stone beads. She said, "Do it yourself? I like your style."

A clerk walked up to the girls. "Hi!" she said. "My name is Jean. Are you finding what you are looking for?"

"Not yet," said Val. She put down a bead she had been looking at. "But we just started to look around. Do you have any glass beads?"

"We have many glass beads," Jean said. She pointed down the block. "They are made right here in town."

Val and Tess traded glances. "We were just talking about this," said Tess. "How is glass made?"

It turned out that Jean knew a lot about glass. "To make glass, you need sand, heat, and ashes," she said. Jean told them more. First you mix ashes with the sand. Then you heat the mix higher and higher. The sand gets so hot it melts. "It turns runny," said Jean. "Like the stuff you pour on pancakes."

"Glass comes from grains of sand?" asked Val. "That seems so odd."

"Strange, huh?" said Jean. The kind of ash used changes the glass, said Jean. It made the glass white or green or sometimes clear.

"You say the glass gets runny," said Tess. "So how can you make a bead with it?"

"You pour it into a mold," said Jean. "The mold can be nearly any shape. When it cools, it is no longer runny. The glass is hard. Just like these!" Jean picked up a jade green bead.

Jean said glass has been made for at least 3,000 years. It was hard to make it right. So glass was very rare. This meant that glass cost a lot, too. In the old days of Rome, only the rich had glass.

Val saw a glass vase in the store. "But how would you make a glass jar or something like this?" she asked.

"That is where glass blowers come in. They blow air into melted glass," said Jean. The two girls just looked at her. "I told you before. They make glass like this right here in town."

Jean showed the girls an ad. The ad was taped to the shop door. Tess read the ad out loud. It told about a glass blowing class. It said that the glass blowers taught classes on glass. You could learn to make things with hot glass. Best of all, the class was free!

"Nice price," said Val.

"How very D.I.Y.," said Tess. She gave Val a smile. "I need to make something with glass."

"Is it for yourself?" said Val.

"Nope," said Tess. "It is a gift for someone else."

Val laughed. The trip to the bead shop had been a hit with Tess.

CHAPTER 3

E-mail from Tess

> **From:** Tess Sharp
>
> **To:** Val Chase, Sam Tripp, Nate Parks
>
> **Subject:** Hot Glass

Hi, all. Val took me to the bead shop called Beads and Stuff. Sam, you would have liked it. They had some strange stuff! Anyway, we learned something there. A place here in town makes things out of glass. They make glass beads, bowls, vases, glasses, jars, and glass art, too. Some are small. But some of their art is huge!

The way these things are made is by "glass blowing." That sounds pretty odd, huh? I wanted to learn more about this. Lucky for me, the glass blowers give a free class. So I thought, "Why not?" Plus, there is something I need to make out of glass. So I asked my dad to drive me to the glass blowing place.

When we walked into this place, the first thing we felt was HEAT. That is one hot spot! My dad started to sweat right away. It felt like there was a wall of heat. The heat comes from the stoves they use. The stoves heat the glass to make it soft and runny. Want to know how hot glass has to be to get soft? Over 2,000 degrees!

You should check this place out. Dad and I got to watch the glass blowers work. That way, you learn how things are done. A worker tells you how they make things at the shop. The glass blowers all wear thick glasses. They have to wear big mitts and long sleeves. These keep them safe from the heat. And trust me, those stoves are HOT!

The first stove melts the glass in a pot. It gets thick and runny. The glass blowers put a long steel pipe in the soft glass. They turn the pipe and pick up a gob of glass. The pipe and melted glass are pulled out of the stove. The glass glows red hot at the end of the pipe!

The soft glass starts to cool. It does this as soon as it is out of the stove. The glass blowers start blowing into the cool end of the pipe. The air goes into the gob of glass at the other end. This makes the glass get bigger.

The blowers shape the glass. They do this in two ways. They can roll the pipe with its gob of melted glass on a flat piece of steel. Or they use wet wood tools. The glass may get too cool and hard to work with. The

They can roll the pipe with its gob of melted glass on a flat piece of steel.

blowers put the pipe into a bigger stove. The glass blob heats up and gets softer. This is done over and over to get the shape just right.

At last a piece is done. Now it goes in the third stove called a "kiln." This stove is used to cool the glass. It might take hours or days to cool the glass. And it must be cooled slowly. If it is not, the glass will crack or break. When these stoves turn off, the glass is cool.

Anyway, I loved watching the glass blowers and seeing the things they made. It was so cool! Well, not "cool," but you know what I mean. I can't wait to try making something myself. This could be

our best film yet!

See you tomorrow.

Tess

CHAPTER 4

Glass Break Down

The next day the team was in film class. Tess asked, "Did you get my e-mail?"

"I did," said Val. "It sounds like you are pretty brave. Making something out of melted glass! What are you going to make?"

Before Tess could say, Sam cut in. "Pretty dumb is more like it," he said. "The glass will be 2,000 degrees!

How scary is that?"

Nate winked at Tess. He said, "It is very

scary, Sam. You should come with me today. I have a safe way for us to film glass." Nate had made some phone calls. He had found a place where old glass was taken. He had asked to go there. "It is called the Re-Use It Place. We can film the glass coming in. We can see how glass is re-used," said Nate.

Sam thought this sounded fine. "Sure, I will come with you," he said.

Val turned to Tess. "Why don't you come with me to class? Mrs. Roble has something she wants us to see."

The two girls left for class. Nate and Sam got the film stuff set to go. "How will we get to the Re-Use It Place?" asked Sam.

Nate looked outside. A large truck had just pulled into the parking lot. "Our ride is here now," he said. Sam gave him an odd look. Nate said, "They were glad to take us. They want someone to make a film about re-using things."

The two boys went outside. They walked up to the truck. Sam knew the truck. He had seen it before. "Hey, I know this truck!" He said. "This truck picks up stuff at my curb each week!"

"That's right," said the truck driver. He shook hands with the boys. "This is where your old cans, glass, and such go."

The truck's driver was named Zed. He was glad the boys were making a film. Zed showed them the parts of the truck. There was a place for cardboard. There was a place for cans. And there was a place for glass.

"My job is to get folks to re-use stuff like glass," Zed said. "That way it does not get thrown away. Many people re-use glass, but 5 percent of all trash is still glass," said Zed. "That needs to come down to 0 percent. Then I will be glad." Sam asked Zed to say more. He wanted to get Zed on film.

Zed stood by his truck. He looked right at Sam. "There would be less waste if all glass was re-used," he said. "Glass takes 1,000,000 years to break down into sand. So if glass gets thrown away, it does not go away. It just sits in

"My job is to get folks to re-use stuff like glass," Zed said.

a landfill."

"Great!" said Sam.

The three of them got in the truck. They headed to the Re-Use It Place. On the way, Zed told them about his job. He carried most types of glass on his truck. Clear glass and colored glass were the best to re-use. It was harder to work with things like broken glass or light bulbs. And some folks asked to re-use odd things. One time, a man wanted Zed to re-use the windshield from his car!

They pulled into the Re-Use It Place. Nate and Sam saw many trucks like Zed's. They pulled up to a spot. There the truck could unload its stuff. Zed pointed to a door.

"Someone is waiting for you," he said.

The two boys went inside. A girl named Sarah met them there. She gave them hard hats, eyeglasses, and earplugs. "We don't want you to have any bad luck while you are here," Sarah said.

CHAPTER 5

Glass Class

Val and Tess were in the art room. The class was working hard on a job. Mrs. Roble had put some pieces of glass on a large shelf. The glass was stained in shades of green, blue, and red. Tess picked up a piece of green glass. She held it up to her eye.

"Like green specs!" Tess said.

Mrs. Roble came over. "Hold it up to the light," she said. Val picked up a piece of blue glass. She went to where sunlight came in the classroom. Val held the glass to the sunlight and looked.

The blue glass lit up. It looked as if it were plugged in.

"Wow!" Val said.

"There is nothing like stained glass," said Mrs. Roble.

Tess said, "This may sound dumb. But how does glass get stained?"

"Maybe something spilled on it," said Val. Then she made a face. "Ouch. That's a joke Sam would make."

Mrs. Roble laughed. She told the girls that a kind of dust stained the glass. The dust could be made from many things like tin, lead, or gold.

Mrs. Roble said the dust was added in two ways. One makes a glass of even color. To do this, add the dust when the glass is runny.

The other way is good for making patterns. This happens when the dust is added to cooler glass. Then the glass gets reheated.

The two girls picked up more glass. Each piece was not the same. Some pieces felt smooth. Some pieces had bumps. Some had waves. Some felt scratchy in their hands.

"Wow!" said Val. "They do not even feel the same as each other."

"No two pieces are the same," said Mrs. Roble. "We like to use stained glass in this class. It helps to make each piece of art one of a kind."

Tess and Val walked around. They watched how the glass was being used. The art class was putting the pieces of stained glass into wood frames. They fit the pieces so they were side by side. Each piece of stained glass had to fit. Then they glued the pieces on a wood backing. Some folks added bits of tile with the glass. When the artwork was done, it looked like a stained glass jigsaw.

Val stood back. "When you are close, all you see is stained glass," she said. "But if you step back, it looks like something else."

When the artwork was done, it looked like a stained glass jigsaw.

The two girls took turns. They looked at the jigsaws and stepped back. "This one looks like the sun," said Tess. "It is rising on a hilltop."

Val squinted her eyes. "This one looks like a fish in a stream."

"I like these," said Tess. "But what are they used for?"

Mrs. Roble came by. "These glass jigsaws are pretty to look at," she said. "But stained glass can be used lots of ways. Have you seen stained glass in a church?" The girls nodded. "Folks have made that kind of art for nearly 1,000 years. The stained glass is part of a wall. It keeps the cold out. But it lets the light in. And stained glass is used in lampshades, too."

The two girls walked back to film class. They had written down a lot of notes on stained glass. They talked about what they had seen.

"That was neat," said Tess. "It made me think of something. Now I know what I will make with the glass blowers."

"Good for you. And what will that be?" asked Val.

Tess just shook her head. "You will have to wait and see," she teased.

CHAPTER 6

New from Old

It was the next day in class. The team had a lot to talk about. Sam and Nate told the girls what they had seen at the Re-Use It Place. First, the trucks dumped out the glass. Then the glass was sorted by type. The same types of glass were put on long moving belts. These brought the glass into a spot where it was crushed.

"You should have heard it!" said Sam. "The sound of breaking glass filled that place."

"Was it safe?" joked Tess.

Sam shook his head. Nate rolled his eyes. "I didn't think so. But we are brave, you know. So we got some good film."

After the glass was crushed, it was washed. The glass had to be clean for its next step: a trip to a huge stove! There, the broken glass was heated up higher and higher. When the glass melted, it could be poured into molds for things like jars. The hot glass cooled off. And a new jar had been made with old glass.

"The new jars are sent out to be filled and used again," said Nate.

"Let me see if I get this," said Val. "Old jars are brought to the Re-Use It Place." Nate and Sam nodded. "They break the jars, clean them, melt them, and make new jars." Nate and Sam nodded again.

"But why not just re-use the old jars as they are?" asked Val.

Nate looked at Sam. Sam looked back at Nate. "We did not think to ask that," Nate said.

They all laughed. The girls then told Nate and Sam about the glass art they had seen.

"We should go back there after school. We can get some art on film," said Tess. She went to get the film stuff.

Nate called out to her. "Speaking of glass art, when can we see you blow glass?"

Tess turned around. "I am going to make something this weekend!" she said.

"What is she going to make?" asked Sam in a low voice.

"She won't say," said Val. "And I am dying to find out."

CHAPTER 7

Glass for Pip

Nate, Tess, and Val were at Sam's house again.
Sam was cooking on the grill. He walked slowly
in and out the sliding door each time.

Inside, Val had turned on the TV. She found
a show called "D.I.Y. TV."

Sam was at the grill when Nate yelled
loudly. "Oh my gosh, Sam, get in here!!"

Sam said. "Why all the yelling, Nate?"

"Look!" Nate said. He pointed to the TV. It
showed the Re-Use It Place. Then a girl came

on the screen.

"That's Sarah!" said Nate to Tess and Val.

Sarah was talking. She was telling why the glass jars had to be crushed. Those who use lots of glass jars needed them in all sizes. It would take too much time to look at all the jars to find what they need. That was why the jars were sorted, cleaned, crushed, and made into new jars. Whole batches of jars of the right size could be made at once.

"Now I get it," said Val. After the show was over, the team had a bite to eat. Then Sam got set to show their film. Val had changed it the day before. She had added a last scene. The boys did not know about it.

41

The group sat down, and the show started. There were scenes in the bead store and the Re-Use It Place. There was one on Mrs. Roble's class. The four film makers liked what they saw.

Then the last scene came on. It showed Tess. She was at the glass blowing place with her dad. Nate and Sam were shocked. "What is this?" they wanted to know. "When did you add this?" they asked. Val and Tess laughed and laughed at their prank.

"Boy, was your dad sweating!" said Nate.

"I know," Tess said. She rolled her eyes.

On screen, Tess turned to one of the workers. She asked him his name. The worker's name was Lee. Lee blew glass the same way it was done 2,000 years in the past. Lee said that lots of things were made from glass. He said glass was used in sports, too.

Lee smiled. "When kids play hoops, glass is used. The backboard is made of glass." Lee then showed Tess a glass baseball bat he had made.

Next, Tess got set to make her glass piece. First, she put on the glasses she needed to be safe. Then, she took a pipe. Lee helped her reach the pipe into the hot stove full of melted glass. As the two worked, the piece slowly took shape. At last, it was done. Lee put on some mitts. He held up Tess's piece. He did this before putting it into the kiln to cool. The team saw what Tess had made.

"It's a blue glass jar!" said Sam. "But why did you need to make a jar?"

"I told you," said Tess. "I needed to make something for a pal. Well, Pip is a mouse and also a pal. His drinking jar had a crack. So I wanted to make him a new one."

"You learned how to blow glass for a MOUSE?" asked Nate. "Tess, you are a true pal."